KING FRANK

AND THE KNIGHTS OF THE ECOQUEST

KING FRANK
AND THE KNIGHTS OF THE ECOQUEST

BY

MARTIN KISZKO

ILLUSTRATIONS BY SARAH VONTHRON-LAVER

First published in 2021 by Martin Kiszko.
Contact: contact@greenpoemsforablueplanet.com
www.greenpoemsforablueplanet.com
www.martinkiszko.com

ISBN 978-0-9568549-6-4

British Library Cataloguing-in-Publication Data:
A catalogue record for this book is available from
The British Library.

Book design and typesetting by Simon Bishop.
Typeset in DeRoos and Celtic Hand.
Printed in the Czech Republic via Akcent Media.

For All Those On Their Ecoquests

KING FRANK AND THE KNIGHTS OF THE ECOQUEST

CALLIOPE THE MUSE

In ancient times a poet didn't know it all!
  He or she would make an invocation, like a call,
  To one of several goddesses known as a muse —
Who would come up with a story the poet might use!
A poet would ask Calliope, that's me —
The muse of epic poetry,
To bless the words, lines,
And music of an epic rhyme.
So as goddess, I'll fire the arrow of inspiration
Plus character information,
And the poet's pen will the tale begin
Of three knights: two heroes and a heroine.
Our title *King Frank and the Knights of the Ecoquest*.
Harold and Haroldia the heralds will tell you the rest.

HAROLD THE HERALD

At the far end of Earth,
To the far right of the Lost Lands of Slank,

HAROLDIA THE HERALD

And a bit further on
Past the shops and bank...

HAROLD THE HERALD

Was the Kingdom of Frank.

HAROLDIA THE HERALD

Now Frankdom's land was polluted and rotten,
  Its kingdom and people had long
        been forgotten.

Customs and costume, conversation and rhyme,
Had barely moved on since medieval times!
And whether a blessing or whether a curse,
Their speech was only delivered in verse!
The kingdom's environmental situation was drastic,
A throwaway culture that chucked away plastic:
   Bottles, containers, bags, trays,
   Which made piles of trash day after day.
   On top of all that and of not much worth,
Were defunct mobiles thrown out from the rest of Earth,
Which the kingdom's folk scavenged in the hope that a few
Had a signal to send a text or two.

HAROLD THE HERALD

But back to the description and set up of plot.
Close to the centre in a majestic spot
Was the imposing Castle Camalcott.

Some said it was the original site
Of Camelot, where King Arthur and his knights
Sat around the round table night after night.
Others said it was named after Princess Katiena of Alcott,
But whether that legend was true or not,
The family who lived at Camalcott
Was King Frank, king of all Frankdom, and Eileen his queen
With their daughter Princess Aqualine.

HAROLDIA THE HERALD

Now Aqualine, at the age of eighteen,
Said goodbye to the king and queen,
As what she longed for most of all
Was to travel beyond the castle walls.
So, one morning she left her royal abode
And out of the castle gates she rode.

HAROLD THE HERALD

Six months later a litter arrived.
The castle drawbridge opened wide.
As the royal court watched on teary-eyed,
The king's physician ushered the princess inside.

KING'S PHYSICIAN

From her travels in the kingdom's furthest parts,
Our princess returns with a weak heart.
Princess Aqualine your precious daughter
Was poisoned by dirty drinking water.
I've used every medicine here
For her high temperature and diarrhoea.

HAROLD THE HERALD

For several feverish nights and days
She tossed and turned then silent lay.
Was she dead or still alive?
Could she beat the sickness and survive?
One Monday morning Aqualine
Awoke from her illness...

PRINCESS AQUALINE

I had a dream,

HAROLD THE HERALD

Was the first thing she said to the king
and queen.

Princess Aqualine

I dreamt we were drowning, we couldn't survive.
We were caught in a deluge
And feared for our lives.
Waves and waves of bottles and trays
Tumbled and crashed and fell in our way.
We couldn't escape overflowing bins,
Bags and wrapping entangled our limbs.
Our water was poison, unfit to drink,
Dirty and foul with a stench and a stink.

Queen Eileen

It's so very true.
One dream interpretation I have for you
Is that the situation is getting drastic,
Parts of our castle are covered in plastic.
Homes in the kingdom are full of it too,
So much junk — what shall we do?

Princess Aqualine

We can't sit around or hesitate,
We must act now before it's too late.
Father my king heed these words I pray,
To save the kingdom we must change our ways.
Bad times are upon us, the matter is dire,
Mountains of trash getting higher and higher.

There's not a single empty bin.
Can't you see the mess we're in?
This is a most serious situation,
Even our castle has poor sanitation.
Like the illness I had, it's plain to see
Your kingdom could become as sick as me.

HAROLD THE HERALD

The king paced about like kings often do,
Very soon he felt low with the royal blues.

KING FRANK

What I hear from my dear daughter
Is that we are living without safe clean water.
I know you're right. What can we do?
My kingdom will turn into trash and poo.

PRINCESS AQUALINE

Here's a proposal I'd like to submit.
I don't care if your advisors think it unfit,
But we require a knight or two or three
To venture forth in bravery,
To find whatever eco-treasure
Will give us all immeasurable pleasure,
And fuel an eco-revolution
That becomes our kingdom's green solution.

KING FRANK

The situation is truly bleak.
What is this treasure of which you speak?

PRINCESS AQUALINE

I remember a story my nurse often told
When I was a girl, only seven years old,
Once long ago in our kingdom's land
Was a source of fresh water close at hand.
A spring from the earth, crystal and pure,
Now gone — its location remembered no more.
You ask me of what eco-treasure I speak,
The ancient Fountain of Frank is what we must seek.

HAROLD THE HERALD

And to that end the king agreed.

KING FRANK

We shall advertise for the knights we need.
Each shall be chosen at royal behest
To venture forth on an ecoquest
To prove their best to my Aqualine
And to King Frank and Queen Eileen.
They must vow to return with eco-solutions
For the Kingdom of Frank's water pollution.

12

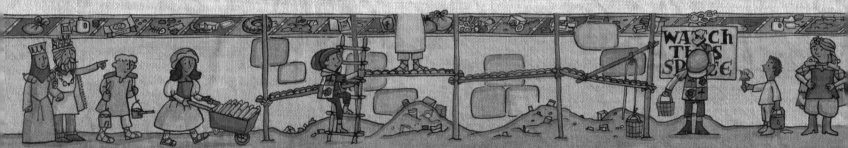

PRINCESS AQUALINE

All Frankdom's land must be environmentally sound
With healthy soil and a litter-free ground.
But one eco-treasure the knights must bring
Of special importance to my king —
Who will honour them with riches and rank —
Is the lost Fountain of Frank.
A source of water pure beyond measure
To change the lives of people forever.

KING FRANK

I think I know who should write
A royal advert for three knights.
Lester the Jester has the know-how and wit
To create an advert that will be a hit.

HAROLD THE HERALD

So Lester was summoned and brought pen and pad
To compose job specs for the hire-a-knight ad.

LESTER THE JESTER

Wanted! Three gallant knights to ride abroad
With own armour and sword,
A shield of course,
And preferably a horse.
Apply only if you're professional knights
Who will trot, canter and gallop for days and nights
Across deserts and mountains, swamps and rivers,
Against monster or army, you must never quiver.
And you'd better make sure at the end of the quest
You return with an eco-treasure chest;
Eco-treasure to help the kingdom's plight.
The jobs will go to the most eco-friendly knights.

WANTED
MUST HAVE FOLLOWING · THREE GALLANT KNIGHTS TO RIDE ABROAD
ARMOUR AND SWORD | SHIELD | OWN HORSE | DIPLOMA IN KNIGHTING | P.K.O PROFESSIONAL KNIGHT QUALIFICATION
PLEASE TICK ALL RELEVANT BOXES

HAROLDIA THE HERALD

On an evening out at a knightclub,
Three local knights saw the advert pinned up.
First Leofrik, poet knight, wordsmith of the three,
Armed with the kingdom's best poetry.
Second, Catrain the courageous brave knight
Who believed no warrior could challenge her might.
The third was Alf, the best dressed of knights,
Who was proud his mum knitted his chainmail and tights.
Also known as the fainthearted hypochondriacal knight,
Alf complained of a cold when confronted to fight.
Leofrick started their idle wondering...

14

LEOFRICK

If we applied for this quest-based wandering, what is it
we'd find to please the king?

ALF

Can't think of anything.

LEOFRICK

Not surprising.
A treasure trove of bling?
A new crown or a ring?
What are we expected to bring
To impress the king?

HAROLD THE HERALD

In Catrain's head something went ping!

CATRAIN

No, it's this environmental thing
They mention here. So it must be something —
An eco-thing — that would va voom and zing
To totally wow the princess and king.

Alf

Can't think of a thing.

Haroldia the Herald

The advert was answered by the trio of knights.
Each told of past deeds, their jousts and their height.
A few days later, as they dined and drank mead,
The king's messenger arrived on a white steed.

King's Messenger

For your knight application our monarch sends thanks.
I've a royally sealed letter from King Frank.
On the fourth day of this month at half past two
You've been granted a royal job interview.

Harold the Herald

It got to the day and it got to the time,
The knights waited their turn in a long knightly line.

Then a page appeared and called them in
To the chambers of the queen and king.
Princess Aqualine was also there,
With pen and pad at her desk and chair,
She took a few notes from the knights' CV
Then asked...

Princess Aqualine

What experience do you have of quests you three?

Leofrick

I've quested in England, in Ireland and France.
I've fought with all weapons; my favourite's a lance.
I've written of these adventures of mine,
And I'd write of this quest in versical lines.
When the journey is good or the going gets worse,
Every part of the trip I'll recite in verse.
As knight poet I'll tell of the trials and the tests
We endured to complete a successful quest.

HAROLD THE HERALD

Alf was nervous, fainthearted and weak.
He had nothing to say and was next to speak.
Catrain whispered a piece of advice in his ear,

CATRAIN

Make something up or we'll lose the job here.

ALF

For my Kingdom of Frank I'll fight to the last.
I once fought a dragon with my leg in a cast;
I beat seven monsters with a paper clip
After questing through mountains on my bad hip.
Once up against giants I was Alf the bold,
Defeating them even though I had a cold.
One time, when my eyes were infected and twitched,
I wrestled a demon, a troll and a witch.
My mum always told me 'to no creature yield'.

Her words and her photo emblazon my shield.
I also sponsor an endangered newt
And have passed an exam on the lute.
Did I mention my embroidery class?
Or the visor I'm making out of stained glass?

CATRAIN

I know I said grovel
Not recite your latest novel!
Like my co-knights I have knightly abilities.
I've mastered all of the knightly agilities:
Tournament jousting, long jumping, diving, swimming,
Wrestling, weaponry, climbing, dancing.
These feats can be done by milkmaid or farmer,
But I do all these things whilst wearing my armour.

16

Princess Aqualine

It's very knightly
That you can move sprightly
In all that metal. I commend your ability
But my knights must also have the facility to master
all the eco-agilities:
The knowledge of what makes clean air,
The recycling of stuff we buy, use or wear,
Reducing carbon on all of your quests,
Leaving wildlife in lairs and birds in their nests.
Most importantly I, the king's daughter,
Ask you to find us safe clean water.
My father the king will contract the deal
For your reward on return and expenses for meals.

King Frank

But one final demand the king makes alone:
Can you lift the bin no other can lift from the sacred Binstone?

Harold the Herald

So the court and the crowds filled the streets
To watch the knights attempt the feat.

17

BEAN BROTH

KING FRANK

Never before as a group or alone
Has any knight lifted the bin from the Binstone,
But any who pass this demanding test
Will be knights who are worthy to take on the quest.

HAROLD THE HERALD

The knights took their turn to lift up the bin,
But each knight alone couldn't move the thing.

ALF

My osteopath said I shouldn't try
To lift on my own as I've wobbly weak thighs.

HAROLD THE HERALD

Yet on a final attempt with six hands and Alf's cry,
The bin left the stone and was raised up high.

KING FRANK

Knights of the bin-lift from the Binstone
You are revered by the people, the court and the throne.
The royal family has thus decreed
The job of the quest is won by these three.
In these circumstances I expect you are guessing
I'll grant one of my frankly incredible blessings.
Kneel, brave knights of the ecoquest.
I pray on this mission you'll be truly blessed.
Arise quickly now as I don't wish to get
Knee dents in my royal carpet.

PRINCESS AQUALINE

Go forth, be strong, be bold, be brave.
It is our future you must save.
Find the lost ancient pure Fountain of Frank,
And the kingdom and I will bestow our thanks.

With climate change upon us now
You will surely to the elements bow.
Extreme weather may quell the quest.
Make sure you take gloves, long pants and a vest.
Remember your mobile reception will fail
As you venture forth on the forest trail.

HAROLDIA THE HERALD

The quest began the following day.
Princess Aqualine waved them away.
Catrain saluted and touched her heart,
While a nervous Alf let out a fart.
Leofrick vowed to do his best
And continued his poem about the quest.

LEOFRICK

Out of the Kingdom of Frank they rode,
Avoiding endangered hedgehogs on rocky roads.
Do you know those two lines ending r-o-d-e and r-o-a-d,
rode and road, have identical rhyme — rode and road.
Different meanings and spellings these two words possess
Such words are called homophones...

CATRAIN AND ALF

Leofrick give it a rest!

HAROLDIA THE HERALD

They galloped past streams, rivers and lakes,
Through pools and alongside mountain cascades,
Across country paths and winding lanes,

ON A JOURNEY THREE BRAVE KNIGHTS ALL SPORTING BRAVE KNIGHT TIGHTS

ZZZZzzzz

19

Amidst howling winds and pounding rain.
Villagers and travellers they chanced upon
Greeted the knights with garlands and song:

VILLAGERS

King Frank and the knights of the ecoquest!
King Frank and the knights of the ecoquest!

CATRAIN

Great green gratitude and knightly thanks
For supporting our quest and the Kingdom of Frank!

HAROLDIA THE HERALD

As evening drew close and birds took to their nests,
So did the knights who longed for a rest,
And in the chilly toe-numbing hours of night
With only a campfire for warmth and light,

They were glad the princess at her behest
Made them take gloves, long pants and a vest.

LEOFRICK

It's not every day one's given the mission
To go on a *questurial* expedition.
That's a new word I've just created;
As a wordsmith I should be congratulated!

HAROLDIA THE HERALD

But the others were tired of poetry tips
And longed for a meal, a drink and a kip.
The next morning, they set out at first light.
Catrain considered the paths...

CATRAIN

Let's take a right.
I'm pretty sure this track will be shorter...

HAROLD THE HERALD

But their way was blocked by a stretch of water.

LEOFRICK

There's a pong in the air which smells like poo.

CATRAIN

Alf you ate beans, sure it's not you?

ALF

Cross my heart
I'd never fart
When riding alongside you two.
But I agree it does smell like poo!

HAROLD THE HERALD

Ahead was a river that flowed in slow motion;
A waterway of yellowy-brown pollution.
At the riverside an old man dozed
Aside a sign: 'Ferry Closed'.

LEOFRICK

Wake up, good sir! Leofrick, Alf, and Catrain call.
May we cross over before evening falls?
We are knights in search of the lost Fountain of Frank.
Could you specially for us put out the gangplank?

TERROWIN THE FERRYMAN

I don't wish to cause you worry,
But good knights be not in a hurry.
Rest now. Perhaps order a takeaway curry.
My name is Terrowin. You can call me Terry.
It's been many long years since I ran the ferry.

ALF

That's just as well Terry as I've often been sick
When travelling by raft, rowboat or ship.
With my bad back and my dodgy left hip,
My travel insurance won't cover the trip.

HAROLD THE HERALD

Across the river were houses and barns.

CATRAIN

Surely this river caused that village much harm?

22

TERROWIN THE FERRYMAN

So true, because there's no sanitation or loos!
The river is full of untreated poo
That folk in yonder village do.
So, if you want to go, form an orderly queue.
When the rain comes down and the floods set in,
Poo leaks to the river — fills its banks to the brim.
There's no power to run the treatment plants.
Those they have are often unmanned,
So the dirty water builds up there,
Runs to the soil, and heads for here.

LEOFRICK

Now that you've got that lot off your chest,
Can't you see we are knights on a top-level quest?

TERROWIN THE FERRYMAN

It's not only poo,
But pesticides, chemicals, toxins too.
For a river, that's quite a lethal brew.
Wouldn't dip a toe into that, would you?

LEOFRICK

Very informative, my poo-knowledgeable friend,
But can't we cross here at the river's bend?

TERROWIN THE FERRYMAN

Well, some have tried swimming and choked with
the smell.
Others that tried were pee-drenched as well.
You can see there are many dung heaps to climb
Or you could accept the task of writing a rhyme.
Stories are told time after time
Of those who accepted this challenge of mine.
But heed! Many perished in poo, slime and worse
By not coming up with suitable verse!

CATRAIN

Thanks for the offer with which we will stick.
We have a knight of the rhyme, poet Leofrick.

(24)

TERROWIN THE FERRYMAN

You may cross the river if this you can do:
Compose an amusing clerihew.
If it works and it rhymes, it's safe to go through.
Do you know how to write a clerihew?
It's a poem with only four lines:
Lines one and two must end in rhyme,
Lines three and four must also rhyme,
And what will take you extra time —
Create a character in the first line.
Furthermore, in terms of style,
It must be a poem that makes us smile.
Invented by Edmund Clerihew Bentley —
Write as well as him and you'll pass over gently.

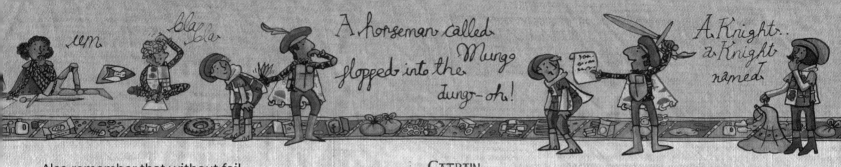

Also remember that without fail,
The poem must tell the river's tale!
I'll take you across if you do all that,
In my pedal-propelled sink, toilet and bath.

HAROLDIA THE HERALD

The knights set about creating their verse
With parchment and pen and lashings of mirth.

LEOFRICK

I think this river of pee and poo
Should be introduced in line two.

CATRAIN

For the first line's character I'm racking my brain.
Anyone got an idea for a name?

ALF

What about Peter or Arthur, Cedric or Quinn,
Or Eleanor, Rose, Thea, Jasmine?

HAROLDIA THE HERALD

Ten minutes passed and then a few more.
How long would it take them to get to line four?
Then Leofrick thrust his sword in the air...

Leofric

We've the character and the two couplets in there!
   Good ferryman all is done that you asked,
   We've completed the compose-a-clerihew task.

Terrowin the Ferryman

Well let's see what you've got as my standards are high.
If it works you cross over or knight knight bye bye.

Leofric

Be impressed good sir by my versical craft
As I deliver my clerihew final draft:
A knight Cedric who searched for a loo,
Fell into a river of poo,
It had filled up from fields and nearby locations,
With the sewage of people with no sanitation.

Catrain

Surely that merits a standing ovation?

Terrowin the Ferryman

Congratulations! You've done it on this occasion.

Haroldia the Herald

Now Terrowin's vessel was an engineering feat
Of tubes, pipes, and a bathroom suite!
On the toilet pan is where Terrowin steered,
With the knights in the bath and sink at the rear.

Terrowin the Ferryman

We'll flush our way over with pedal power,
I'll return for the horses in half an hour.
To launch us away give a firm pedal push,

Each of you row with a toilet brush.
Before we depart, I have one more ask.
Pull down your visor or wear one of my masks!

Haroldia the Herald

Through chemicals, poo and pee they pushed
With brushes heavy with toxic slush.
The crossing was arduous, perilous and tough.
Alf felt sick and was looking quite rough.
He stood up for a moment but tripped over his sword,
Off balance, head first, he fell overboard.
In the gurgling sludge his armour turned brown
And he cried...

Alf

Help me before I'm poo-possibly drowned.

Haroldia the Herald

Now there wasn't a life belt, but in less than a beat,
Leofrick ripped off the toilet seat
Which, attached to a length of old rope twine,
Was thrown into the river as a lifeline.
To make matters worse with Alf set asunder,
There were gusts of wind and a clap of thunder.
The heavens broke open, down came the rain,
Terrowin shouted...

Terrowin the Ferryman

Hurricane!
Pull hard on that rope and get him on deck
Or we'll be under this lot as good as shipwrecked.

27

CATRAIN
> Grab hold of it Alf, and we'll haul you in.
> We'll have you out in less than a min.

HAROLDIA THE HERALD
> But poo, rain and wind tossed him about.
> The others could barely hear his shouts.

ALF
> Help me I'm done for. Please don't tell my mum
> I went down in the sewage from villagers' bums.

HAROLDIA THE HERALD
> But as Catrain and Leofrick told Alf not to worry,
> The wind and the rain whiplashed the ferry.
> > In the midst of the squall and in less than a tick...
> > Over the side went Leofrick!

He floundered around, he choked and he spat,
Until he reached the side of the bath.
Then stretching his arm in the violent downpour,
He grabbed hold of the end of a toilet brush oar
That Terrowin held to yank him inside.

TERROWIN THE FERRYMAN
> Now hold onto the side there's still a rough ride.

HAROLDIA THE HERALD
> Alf was still struggling and gave up all hope
> When Catrain's hands slipped off the rope.

CATRAIN
> I need more help in hauling Alf in.
> Can you pull as well? Be quick Terrowin.

HAROLDIA THE HERALD

They battled poo waves, pee splatter and wind,
With a heave-ho and tug, they pulled poor Alf in.
As the storm passed over, they reached the bank,
Still determined to find the Fountain of Frank.
Terrowin sailed back in his bathroom-suite ship
And loaded the horses for their ferry trip.

TERROWIN THE FERRYMAN

Stand by as I dock, let the horses alight
And I'll bid you goodbye, bold smelly knights.
Give thanks to the rain that has showered you clean,
Except for the smell, no one knows where you've been.
I would advise keeping two metres away
From people you meet in the coming days.
Here's soap, wash your hands over here with me;
Twenty seconds or more will keep them germ free!

Ahead there are bogs, swamps and quicksand.
Beware underfoot as you journey this land.

HAROLDIA THE HERALD

As they left, the villagers formed a throng
And burst into celebratory song.

VILLAGERS

King Frank and the knights of the ecoquest!
King Frank and the knights of the ecoquest!

HAROLD THE HERALD

As they arrived at the edge of marshland and bogs,
They were wrapped in a veil of dense dark fog.
Ghostly shapes in the mist appeared,
One place and another then disappeared.
The horses whinnied and stopped outright.
The knights stood firm, their lips closed tight.

A ghostly sound, a scrape, a crack,
A thud and then a thunderous THWACK!
A crumpling, scrumpling, sloshing sound,
Something plodding on the ground,
A tumultuous crunch, an ear-splitting hit!
Then out of the fog a globulous spit
That sprayed Catrain's eyes, mouth and nose
And dripped from her chin down to her toes.

CATRAIN

Did that green saliva feature
Come from the mouth of a disgusting creature?

HAROLDIA THE HERALD

A tiny gap in the fog appeared.
The knights peered through as swamp mist cleared.

Beyond they saw an endless sea
Of plastic, junk and life's debris.
They squinted and stared with goggled eyes
As a gargantuan shape began to rise.
And on the shoreline taller than trees
Is what Catrain called...

CATRAIN

A monstrosity!

LEOFRICK

Any creature seen since I was born
Is dwarfed by this monster's specstupentacular
wowfabsuperical form.
Those are words invented by me Leofrick.

ALF

To look up at this beast puts my neck in a crick.
Is it a griffin, a dragon or whale?

HAROLD THE HERALD

Alf's face grew incredibly pale.
He took a deep
breath, blew
out his cheeks,
Froze to the
spot
and
was
unable
to speak.
The monster screeched
and spat and roared

As Catrain raised her shield and sword.
Hold back! It's stopped to survey the land,
Let's muster our strength my valiant band.

LEOFRICK

I've heard such creatures roam hereabouts.
Which one it is, I have my doubts.
But of those I know, none shall be missed
On my horrible scary monster list.

Haroldia the Herald

In epic poetry it is the tradition
    To write out a list — a lengthy rendition
    That could be quite boring or keep you agog —
    It's known as an 'epic catalogue'
  Of warriors or ships the poet may feature.
In this poem it's Leofrick's list of monstrous creatures.

Leofrick

From our rubbish and trash these monsters were birthed,
Here are the monsters that roam on Earth:
Dumpasaurus,
Rubbishiraptor,
Trashosaurus,
Tatranadon,
Binopterex,
Wasterotops,

Drosserodon,
Garbageasaurus,
Litteropterex,
Detritusaurus,
Junkapoda,
Scrapasaurus,
Landfillersaurus.

Catrain

There's no more time
To talk of monsters or hear rhyme.
In the name of King Frank and Queen Eileen,
And for our kingdom and Princess Aqualine,
Be brave and attack any monster in sight.
Advance and fight with the might of a knight.

ALF

Another option is to depart.
I'd rather not further weaken my heart.
My doctor usually signs me off
With my allergy to monsters which gives me a cough.

Wait! Bide your moment. There's still time
To hear a monster informational rhyme.
Listen and learn as my ballad will broach
Which one of the monsters makes its approach.

Fellow knights and those who will read of our quest,
Of all the monsters that may rise up before us
And strike fear in the hearts and pants of men,
The worst encounter is Landfillersaurus.

These creatures were solely human-made.

Their bodies created from all our stuff:
Debris, waste, chemicals, toxins,
All that and more it swallowed up.

Born in the Kingdom of Landfillonia,
All scrap there formed its skeleton and tail.
Things thrown away increased its power,
Old armour plates formed its scales.

From the Plastific Ocean came its blood supply.
Its lungs exhaled life-threatening gas.
Everything we've ever dumped
Made up its monstrous mish-mashed mass.

The more we fill the world with trash,
More Landfillersauruses will grow
And pollute our planet.
Defeat it we must and onward we go!

33

HAROLD THE HERALD

The other
two knights
were relieved and glad
To have reached the end of Leofrick's ballad,
But no sooner had Leofrick said his last word,
The clash of the knights with the monster was heard.

CATRAIN

Full forward with lances!
I'll take the rump.
Leofrick take the head.
Alf take the hump.
As sure as I'm Catrain
and as eggs is eggs,
We'll take out this
mobile landfill on legs.

ALF

My verruca is rubbing the back of my shoe.
Give me ten minutes then I'll follow you.
My chiropodist warned me it could get this bad
Without a plaster, a dressing and pad.

HAROLD THE HERALD

The knights used their agilities, skills and tactics
To topple the moving mountain of plastic,
But Landfillersaurus's stupendous tail
Shredded Alf's shiny protective
chainmail.
That was the trigger to make
Alf explode,
His brain switched to red
alert beast-wrestling mode.

34

ALF

Hey! That was my best shirt of rings and steel wire
My mum gave to me when I was a young squire.
No monster on Earth gets away with that.
Prepare yourself for hand to hand combat!

HAROLD THE HERALD

Leofrick and Catrain could not join in,
They were held and trapped by the monster's wings.

CATRAIN

Alf you must fight the battle for us.
Defeat the dreaded Landfillersaurus.

HAROLD THE HERALD

Alf looked at the giant quadruped
And in deep contemplation he scratched
his head.

ALF

Wait! I remember a story in the
Greek myths
About the hero Achilles and his mother Thetis.

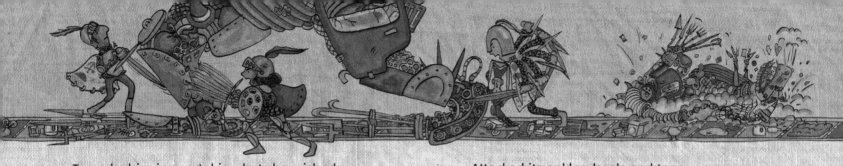

To make him immortal is what she wished;
It could be done by a dip in the river Styx.
But submerged in the water, body stripped bare,
His heel was left stuck up in the air.
And later, when Paris fought Achilles,
He shot poisoned arrows below his knees.
Straight at the heel — Achilles' weak part —
In seconds the poison stopped his heart.
I can see that this monster is also weak
As its ankle joints have a leachate leak!

HAROLDIA THE HERALD

As Landfillersaurus grappled and roared,
Alf gave its ankles a swipe of his sword.
The monster staggered and reeled in pain
Releasing Leofrick and Catrain.
Then the resolute knights with mighty blows

Attacked its ankles, heels and toes,
And with an awesome tremendous crash,
It fell with an almighty splash!
It narrowly missed the victorious three,
And drowned in the ocean of life's debris.
Would the beast rise again from where it had sunk?
Only if humans keep throwing out junk.

HAROLD THE HERALD

Onwards they rode playing I-Spy
Until they spied brooding clouds in the sky.
In minutes the land was marshy with mud
And their socks were soaked by an oncoming flood.
Then out of the forest an eerie form
Stealthily paw-plodded through the storm.
The rain-drenched knights gave a long fixed stare
At a massive majestic polar bear.

Polar Bear

Good knights I am weary, stand not in my way,
For I've traversed sea and land many nights and days.
I've wandered beneath the sun and stars
From the realm of the Arctic, that land afar.

But my habitat was so quick to pass,
My home was destroyed by greenhouse gas.
Alone on an ice floe without wellies or mac,
I survived the melting polar ice cap.

Look over to that mountain range
Also affected by climate change.
Warmer weather makes those glaciers thaw;
Sea levels will rise, waves will lash at your door.

As temperatures rise, snowpack disappears,
So their melt happens earlier in the year.
It means that as the snowpack shrinks,
Supply to our rivers is on the brink.

And as Earth heats up several fold,
It increases the water the atmosphere holds.
Take some other route across this terrain
Lest your journey ends in vain.

37

CATRAIN

But what of you, courageous bear?
Will you journey with us or travel elsewhere?

POLAR BEAR

My journey is over, my paws they are sore,
I'm injured and know I can't walk anymore.

LEOFRICK

As for us, we continue our ecoquest.
Until we find treasure we cannot rest.
Our kingdom is plagued by so much pollution,
We have to press on to find a solution.

We've heard from our princess, queen and king
Of the Fountain of Frank which is fed by a spring.
Fresh clean water for our kingdom's health
So our people can work and create wealth.

POLAR BEAR

It is true such a fountain, many years back,
Was known to the Arctic polar bear pack.
But as our ice homes melted and sank,
We forgot all about the Fountain of Frank.

ALF

Do you remember where it might be?

POLAR BEAR

One day a young cub came up to me
And showed me a map he'd found in the sea.
We thought it had come from an ancient shipwreck
Or was lost on a polar explorer's trek.
On the front was a message, a faded black scrawl,
Which I read out to bears, seals, whales and narwhals.
'This map will look blank to the reader's eyes
Unless the holder can swiftly supply
An acrostic poem the magic map likes —
Then it will reveal the details inside.'
But that careless young bear
Let the wind blow the map into the air,
And a snowy owl out hunting that day
Snatched up the map and hid it away.

I knew the owl and asked her to swap
The map for a lemming, a weasel or fox.
That was the food her owlets preferred.
I also offered her squirrels and birds.

CATRAIN

And did she agree to your food-for-map deal?

POLAR BEAR

She was happy to trade it for such a meal.

LEOFRICK

So do you have the map? Can we see it too?

POLAR BEAR

Only the front will be visible to you.
It's useless unless an acrostic you write,
And if the map likes it, you'll see what's inside.
There's one other challenge that makes matters worse,
The subject of water must be in the verse.

LEOFRICK

We all have minds creative and quick
To come up with a suitable acrostic.

ALF

Sorry to seem a little bit thick,
But what actually is an acrostic?

LEOFRICK

Each letter of a chosen word
Must be the start of a line of the verse.
A water-based theme is required for the map.

CATRAIN

How about the thaw at the polar ice cap?

HAROLDIA THE HERALD

It took a tremendous amount of time
To write their Arctic acrostic rhyme.
Leofrick stood poised and poetically proud,
And to map and companions he read it aloud.

LEOFRICK

Arctic at
Risk as
Climate change
Thaws
Ice
Cap.

A is for arctic, R is for risk, C is for climate change,
T is for thaws, I is for ice and C is for cap.

Arctic at
Risk as
Climate change
Thaws
Ice
Cap.

HAROLDIA THE HERALD

The map started glowing and each corner curled,
The rest of the parchment began to unfurl.
Inside was a drawing of the Kingdom of Frank,
But the fountain's location still drew a blank.

LEOFRICK

This map has a kenning scrawled on its middle,
That's a very short poem that's actually a riddle!
It describes something without giving its name.
This one hides the location of the fountain.

HAROLDIA THE HERALD

Catrain read the kenning and pondered the words.
Alf thought the riddle was somewhat absurd.
Leofrick quizzingly mumbled the rhyme
And read out the lines time after time.

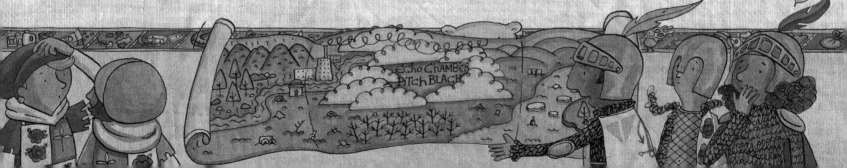

LEOFRICK
Echo chamber.
Pitch black.

CATRAIN
What can it mean?

ALF
Remains to be seen.

POLAR BEAR
Take the map and continue your quest,
I hope you will pass the kenning test.
Remember me and the plight of the ice.
Go safely and well, good gallant knights.

CATRAIN
One moment, there's something missing here.
Come nomads and wanderers with your good cheer.
Spur us on our knightly quest;
Sing heartily of our questurial test!

VILLAGERS
King Frank and the knights of the ecoquest!
King Frank and the knights of the ecoquest!

HAROLD THE HERALD
The undaunted, unshrinking, unflinching three
Set out in the day's sweltering heat.
Beyond them a landscape of desert dunes
And a quest that wouldn't be ending soon.
The searing heat made the knights sweat.

Inside their armour they were smelly and wet.
Their bottled water was down to one.
They were now at the mercy of the sun.
Leofrick and Alf sat down on the sand.

ALF

It's too hot to ride, to sit or to stand.
Not sure we can make it with feet so sore.
We're doomed by the rising temperature.
This is the worst climate for my dry cough;
Let's get these stifling helmets off.

HAROLD THE HERALD

Catrain didn't listen but pointed and warned...

CATRAIN

Move on for shelter here comes a sandstorm.

HAROLD THE HERALD

In minutes the air was swirling with sand.
They could hardly distinguish the sky from the land.
Yet not too far off on ground parched and cracked,
Catrain spotted what looked like a shack —
And stepping out from within:
A camel with a cheesy grin.

CAMEL

Please feel free to use my humble place.
Shelter from the heat on your face.
You're too early if you're here for the CCAC meet —
Climate Change Awareness Club — not here till next week!

43

But in the meantime I can fill you all in
On next week's talk that I'll be giving.
Global warming has caused much more drought
Which has dried up the water holes here and about.
Temperatures soar higher and higher.
We live in fear of increasing wildfires.
This desert is also expanding by miles
And finding water now takes a while.
Those are my main points — there's nothing I missed —
Desertification — you get the gist?

CATRAIN

We'd like to stay for it and give you our thanks,
But we're on a quest for the Fountain of Frank.
We'd like to get on but what we need first
Is water — we're desperate to quench our thirst.

CAMEL

Not far from here there's an oasis
With a spring to drink from and cool your faces.

HAROLD THE HERALD

Up popped Catrain's immediate thought:

HAROLDIA THE HERALD

Could this be the ancient spring they sought?

CATRAIN

Alf, Leofrick did you hear? A spring, what do you think?

ALF AND LEOFRICK

Just get us a drink.

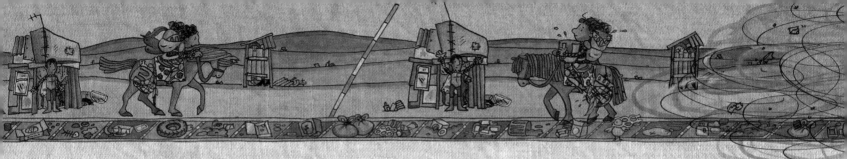

CATRAIN

I'm thinking if this spring is the thing —
And we've finally found it — well here's the sting:
How would we get the spring to the king
And bring our quest to a successful ending?

HAROLDIA THE HERALD

Too tired for questions or a horseback ride,
Sun-stroked Leofrick and Alf stayed inside.
Catrain took their last empty bottle and armoured hats
And tied them on to her horse's back.
Several miles she rode to the spring
And filled bottle and helmets up to the brim.
A few journeys she made, each time filling the hats,
So enough water for knights and horses went back.
Drinking their fill, the knights celebrated
The fact they were now fully hydrated.

CATRAIN

Now that you're better what about my idea?
Consider again the oasis spring here.
Could it be our missing spring?

ALF

If so, how would you pipe its flow to the king?

LEOFRICK

There's no way it can be Frankdom's spring.
Doesn't fit with the description in the kenning.
Echo chamber.
Pitch black.

CATRAIN

Is it a dungeon, a pothole or pit?
What other location could possibly fit?

ALF

An echoey bedroom? A room with no light?

LEOFRICK

I don't think any of those are right.

CATRAIN

What about this: a cave it must be!
We've solved the kenning don't you agree?

HAROLD THE HERALD

The answer was right, the map was aglow,
In seconds the cave's location it showed.

CATRAIN

We've found the location, once and for all,
Unbelievably close to our castle walls.

ALF

Who'd have believed it was there all the time,
Buried beneath all our filth and grime.

HAROLDIA THE HERALD

The journey home was boring and long.
They kept themselves cheerful by singing songs.
Then Alf felt his phone give a vibrate and jitter
And got reception to log into Twitter.

ALF

Just sending a tweet and a text to my mum
To tell her I'm safe and the quest is all done.

LEOFRICK

Send one to the princess while you're online.
Say 'See you on Sunday, we're making good time.'

HAROLD THE HERALD

The knights arrived at the Kingdom of Frank.
Crowds gathered to meet them with greetings and thanks.
Fireworks were launched from the castle's towers;
The knights were bedecked with garlands and flowers.

HAROLDIA THE HERALD

At the gates of the castle the knights raised their swords
To salute the cheering excited hordes.
The portcullis opened and waiting within
Was Princess Aqualine, Queen Eileen and Frank the king.

HAROLD THE HERALD

The royal Frank trumpeters played a fanfare
As pages and squires waved flags in the air.
The knights rode along past the Binstone
And dismounted at the royal thrones.

CATRAIN

Your highnesses we have returned from the quest
With eco-treasure of the very best.
We were challenged by storms, monsters and more,
Survived deserts and seas, we fought on the shores.
On a river of poo our situation was drastic.
Then we rode by the terrible ocean of plastic
Where a Landfillersaurus put us to the test
And almost removed us all from the quest.
A polar bear warned us of climate change,
And we learned that our kingdom must rearrange
Its ways and its methods for dumping stuff.

ALF

And if that wasn't enough,
I had a bad cough!

47

CATRAIN

But that Polar bear
Had a map we have here.
In riddles and rhymes our hearts almost sank,
But we found the location of the Fountain of Frank.

HAROLD THE HERALD

The princess rejoiced and clapped her hands.

PRINCESS AQUALINE

Please tell us more noble knightly band.

CATRAIN

The Fountain of Frank didn't vanish at all.
Its spring is buried near the castle walls!
For hundreds of years, it got covered with trash.
Now's the time to get our fountain back.

HAROLD THE HERALD

Princess Aqualine and the ladies and lords
Joined the crowd in rapturous applause.

KING FRANK

Good knights we must make a celebration
As Pete the Piper our plumber begins excavations.
The fountain's spring must be restored
To pipe clean water for evermore.

HAROLDIA THE HERALD

So, Pete the Piper arrived on the scene,
Ready to plumb for king and queen.

PETE THE PIPER

I'm happy to start the work straight away,
As I lay pipes there's a pipe that I play.
It accompanies my tongue–twisting tongue-tingling hit
That makes me work faster the more that I say it.
Try it yourselves my bold bardic knights
Unless alliterative verse gives you a fright!
Pete the Piper piped a pipe to pipe the water flow.
A pipe to pipe the water flow Pete the Piper piped.
The type of hype about the pipe that Pete the Piper piped,
Was hype that Pete the Piper piped out on a type of pipe!

PRINCESS AQUALINE

Bravo young piper, go forth and plumb
Pipes to all parts of Frankdom.

CATRAIN

But that's not all Princess Aqualine.
We've more eco-treasure that's truly green!

HAROLDIA THE HERALD

The king, queen and princess stared at the knights.

CATRAIN

We've discovered a certain recycling delight!
For years our kingdom got fuller each day
With plastic bottles we all threw away,
But when my knights and horses collapsed in the heat,
I invented this clever recycling feat:
Our three helmets I water-filled up to the brim
From a pool in the desert fed from a spring.

WATER FILLING METHOD DIAGRAM

Then each time I went back and refilled the hats,
I invented refillability — that's what we've brought back.
We don't need to use and throw bottles away,
We only need one we refill every day.

KING FRANK

It's one of the best ideas I've heard.
From this day on I pledge my word
That this idea is truly a wizard no-brainer:
My subjects will have a refillable container.
As for this fearless steadfast three,
They'll be recognised for their bravery.
Your ecoquest we all applaud.

The royal family with one accord
Present the knights with this award:
Three pouches of diamonds and precious gemstones
And land for each to build a home.
Every year your accounts will increase with wealth.
My physician will monthly attend to your health.
In the castle your portraits will be seen.
Is there anything else I've forgotten my queen?

QUEEN EILEEN

Give them new horses, armour and lances,
And we'll invite you to all our parties and dances!

50

ALF

May I beg your pardon, I'll just take the lance.
I've a spinal injury I got at a dance.

HAROLDIA THE HERALD

In a huddle the knights spoke in whispered tones.
Then Catrain approached the royal thrones.

CATRAIN

You are most generous Queen Eileen and King Frank,
For your offer of gifts we express our thanks,
But that money and land we would like you to bank
In an account for the upkeep of the Fountain of Frank.

KING FRANK

Philanthropic knights I'll accept your wish,
In honouring your charity the tradition is this:
You will be dubbed with knightly new names
So that all in the kingdom know of your fame.
Please kneel here before me knights eco-wise
For soon with new eco-names you will arise.
Knight of the Refillable Bottle is Catrain's appellation,
And Leofrick too will be known to our nation
As Knight of the Safe Water Supply.
A final epithet I will apply
To Alf who, though ill, fought valiantly for us.
Rise Sir Knight Monster-Slayer of Landfillersaurus.

SIR ALF KNIGHT MONSTER SLAYER OF LANDFILLERSAURUS

SIR LEOFRICK KNIGHT OF THE SAFE WATER SUPPLY

DAME CATRAIN KNIGHT OF THE REFILLABLE BOTTLE

Queen Eileen

You have shown eco-problems can be solved
When we break our bad habits and have the resolve.
You rose to the challenge and answered our call —
Refills from the fountain for one and all.

King Frank

To remember this day Leofrick you must pen
Our kingdom's brand new national anthem.

Leofrick

A double-dactyl is the poem I'd like to compose.
This is how its format goes:
Each of two verses has four lines,

But here is the thing that will use up my time:
The first line must be two nonsense words.
The second must name someone real or absurd.
The end of line eight must rhyme with line four,
I hope I'm not being a poetry bore.
Line one's syllable plan is three plus three.
Line two is the same. That's easy.
Line three is three plus three again.
Line four three plus one. Don't put down your pen
As line five is a new verse of three plus three.
Line six is even quite tricky for me

52

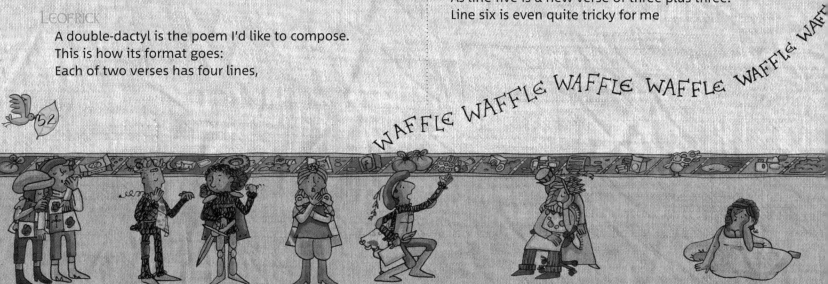

WAFFLE WAFFLE WAFFLE WAFFLE WAFFLE WAFF

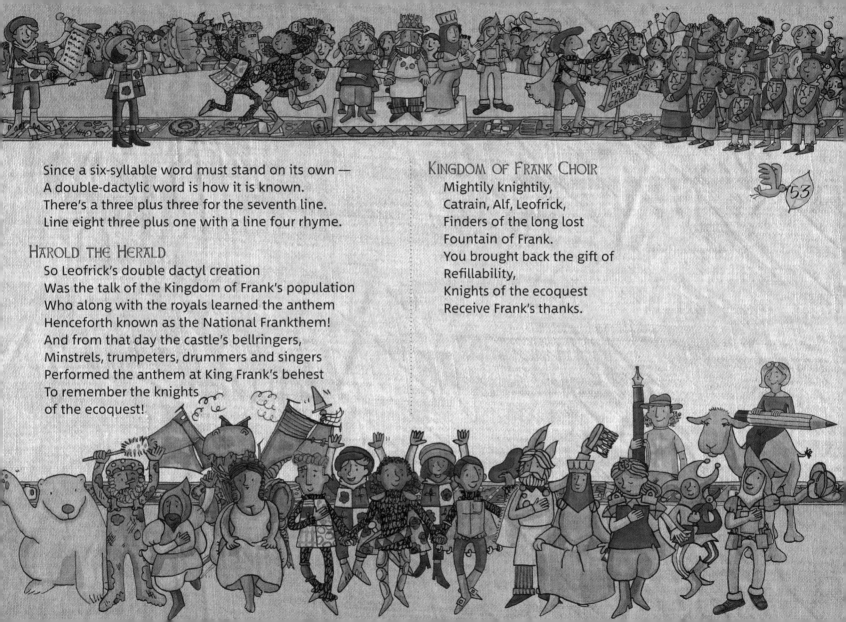

Since a six-syllable word must stand on its own —
A double-dactylic word is how it is known.
There's a three plus three for the seventh line.
Line eight three plus one with a line four rhyme.

HAROLD THE HERALD

So Leofrick's double dactyl creation
Was the talk of the Kingdom of Frank's population
Who along with the royals learned the anthem
Henceforth known as the National Frankthem!
And from that day the castle's bellringers,
Minstrels, trumpeters, drummers and singers
Performed the anthem at King Frank's behest
To remember the knights
of the ecoquest!

KINGDOM OF FRANK CHOIR

Mightily knightly,
Catrain, Alf, Leofrick,
Finders of the long lost
Fountain of Frank.
You brought back the gift of
Refillability,
Knights of the ecoquest
Receive Frank's thanks.

THE END

Acknowledgements

Great green gratitude to Katie Alcott MBE, founder and CEO of charity Frank Water — a charity funding clean water in India and Nepal — who was the inspiration for this epic rhyme! We'd also like to thank Simon Bishop for the design, layout and typesetting of *King Frank and the Knights of the Ecoquest*. Thanks too to John Garrad and Nick Garrad of Akcent Media Ltd and special thanks to proofreaders Michael Bailey, Jane Jones and Clare Thalmann.

KINGDOM OF FRANK